A Season of Sight Words

WINTER

The Sledding Hill

stop
you

by Shannon Penney
Illustrated by Luanne Marten

Scholastic Inc.
New York   Toronto   London   Auckland
Sydney   Mexico City   New Delhi   Hong Kong

ISBN 978-0-545-34431-9

12 11 10 9 8 7   132   20 21 22/0

Printed in the U.S.A.
First printing, November 2011

You can sled!

How do I **stop**?

You will **stop** at the bottom.

Are **you** ready?

You were wrong!

Stop!